Scou the Stray

Clare Helen Welsh

Illustrated by Eve O'Brien

Schofield & Sims

Jayden and Kay were visiting Grandad in his flat.

3

In the car park, the children spied a cat with spots on its fur. It was looking for food.

They got the cat some milk. When there was no milk left, they went to the nearest shop.

The cat tried to come too but it fell on the ground. "Oh dear," said Grandad. "It needs to see the vet."

The vet said the cat had to stay for the night.

Jayden and Kay went back to Grandad's and did some paintings of the cat.

They stuck them up around the car park for people to see.

"That looks like Scout!" cried a man. "She has been missing for days! We found her tag on the road."

When they all went to see the vet the next day, they got a shock.

Jayden and Kay were sad to see Scout go, but they were glad they had helped.

When Jayden and Kay next visited Grandad's, they had fun playing with Scout and her kittens.